An IVF Journey Sailing By Love

Written and Illustrated by
Si Yao Shining Li, Msc

Medical Supervised by
Thomas J.Kim   XingMing Zhong

Qing Xiao   Fang Liu

Art Supervised by
Dan Hu

ISBN:978-0-578-76828-1

用爱承航的IVF旅程

李思瑶 绘著

医学指导 Thomas J.Kim   钟兴明   肖青   刘芳

艺术指导   胡丹阳

Disclaimer

About the Author

Si Yao Shining Li was a Psychometrician in The Psychometrics Center at the University of Cambridge, she is an ACI Certified International Psychological Counselor, and also the member of the British Psychological Society, the Psychometric Society, and Chinese Psychological Society. She founded the Women and Family Counseling Center at Hongkong in 2014. As a women and mother with her own fertility experience, and with her background in cross cultural personality research, she began to focus on how infertility affect women and families cross culturally. Her experiences allowed empathy and understanding to the female who suffer infertile and reproductive disability is not often seen. She established a reproductive counselling program for supporting Chinese families facing fertility difficulties, and further connected the reproductive centers and law organizations in U.S. developed an IMCT (International Multi-disciplinary collaborative Treatment) program, providing patients with information on IVF and third party reproductive programs. These programs help single women/couples successfully face their reproductive program in the U.S. with more positive attitude. Since 2014 she had successfully helped over 50 Chinese couples make their parental dream come true.

关于作者

李思瑶（Shining）女士曾任职于剑桥大学心理测量中心，是ACI认证国际心理咨询师，及英国心理学协会，心理测量学协会，及中国心理学会认证会员。她于2014年在香港成立恆信国际女性家庭关爱中心。同为女性和母亲，她以感同身受的生育经历，以及跨文化人格研究背景，重点关注不孕不育对中国女性及家庭的影响。她对患有不孕症及生殖残障女性的理解，驱动她创立IMCT国际多学科生殖联合项目，与美国生殖中心及生殖法律机构联合，为面临生育困难的中国家庭提供更多有效途径。通过这些辅助生殖联合项目，她为众多中国单身女性/夫妇在进入试管婴儿及第三方辅助生殖计划前，在生殖医疗、心理、法律三方面建立了应有的就医知识和心理建设。

至今，她已成功帮助超过50个中国家庭实现了成为父母的心愿。

Acknowledgement

鸣 谢

I would like to express my special appreciation to Dr. Thomas Jin Kim(RMA SoCal), Dr. Xing Ming Zhong (Family Planning Special Hospital of Guangdong Province), Dr. Qing Xiao(The Eighth affiliated Hospital, Sun Yat-sen University)and Dr. Fang Liu(Shenzhen Maternity & Child Healthcare Hospital) for their supervision in the medical knowledge of this book.

I would like to express my special thanks to artist Dan Hu for his guidance , and Ms. Jia Li Qin(art design student of Macau University of Science and Technology)for her support in completing my drawing, and my appreciation to Hanson International Healthcare team member Ms. Yanni Zhong, Ms. Ge Li and Ms. Jing Lu's association in editing.

I would like to acknowledge the doctors, nurses, psychologists and legal professions who pay their effort to help other fertility dream come true.

特此鸣谢美国生殖医学协会南加州分院Thomas Jin Kim 医生、广东省计划生育专科医院钟兴明医生、中山大学附属第八医院肖青医生、深圳市妇幼保健院刘芳医生对此书医学知识的指导。

特别感谢艺术家胡丹阳先生对此书的艺术指导，以及澳门科技大学艺术生秦嘉励的协助。

感谢恆信国际健康管理有限公司团队成员钟茵、李鸽及卢净对此绘本排版工作的协助。

向所有为成就他人生育梦想而努力的医护人员、心理学家及法律专业人士致敬。

Preface
序言

Child is the most beautiful gift in the world!

孩子是世界上最美丽的恩赐！

This book is dedicated to all the IVF patients who I went through the new-life journey with them. It's my honor could witness them finally become parents. All these IVF journeys are one of the most precious experiences in my life, it made me understand the true love in their marriage is the most powerful strength to overcome all the difficulties of infertility.

此绘本献给所有IVF患者夫妇，有幸能相伴他们完成新生命之旅及见证他们成为父母，是我人生中最珍贵的经历之一。所有的这些IVF旅程让我深刻的体会到夫妻间的爱是克服不孕不育困难最强大的力量。

Mr. and Mrs. Liang knew each other and fell in love since college,

from puppy love to get married,

they always believe love is the basic and result for marriage.

梁先生和梁太太是大学同学，从纯真的校园爱情，

再到携手步入婚姻，他们相信爱是婚姻的一切基础。

They have a very sweet life, soon after they married,
Mrs. Liang's first good news of pregnancy came.

他们生活甜蜜，婚后很快就迎来了梁太太的第一次喜讯。

However, Mrs. Liang's first pregnancy didn't go well,
the fetus' heartbeat stopped on week 9.
In the next following 2 years, luckiness didn't befall in their family,
Mrs. Liang experienced the pain of miscarriage again and again,
they felt very frustrated and helpless.

然而，梁太太的首次怀孕并不顺利，胎儿在9周时没有了胎心。
随后的两年幸运亦没有降临，梁太太一次又一次的不断历经流产之痛。
梁先生和梁太太感到非常失落和无助。

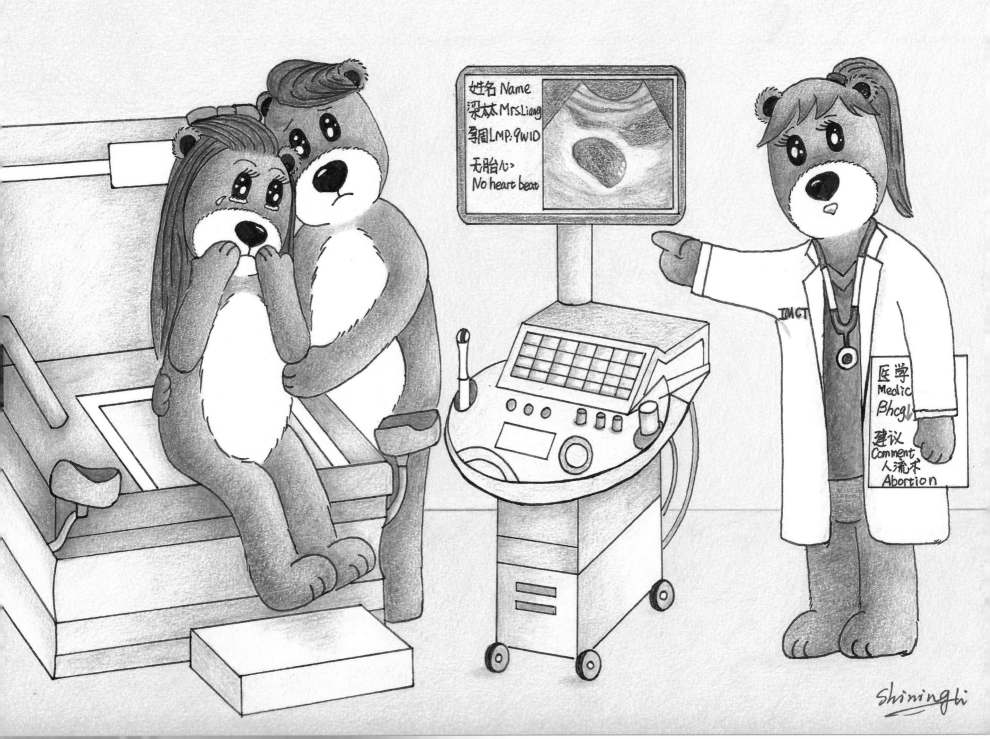

Based on Mrs. Liang's recurrent abortion symptom,
the GYN doctor conducted a comprehensive infertility screening
for Mr. and Mrs. Liang.

医生针对梁太太的复发性流产病史，

为梁先生、梁太太进行了全面和详细的筛查。

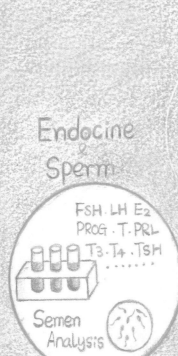

Endocine & Sperm

FSH. LH E₂
PROG. T. PRL
T₃. T₄. TSH
. . . . . .

Semen Analysis

内分泌反精子

Reproductive Structure

生殖结构

Karyotype

生殖体

Reproductive Immunity

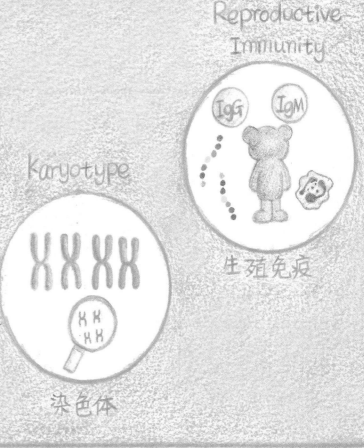

IgG   IgM

生殖免疫

染色体

Infertility Screening

不孕不育筛查

Results
检查结果

Mrs. Liang
梁太太

chiningli

The screening result showed that Mrs. Liang is the chromosome balanced translocation carrier. This would be judged as the key concern to affect their embryo quality and cause miscarriage. The GYN doctor suggested Mr. and Mrs. Liang could consider proceed the IVF program, and further test their blastocysts by PGS, so as to reduce the risk of miscarriage and create a healthy baby. The doctor also suggested them should have a reproductive counseling before they start the program.

根据筛查结果，梁太太属于染色体平衡易位的携带者，
这是影响胚胎质量并造成复发性流产的主要考虑因素。
医生建议，梁先生梁太太可通过IVF方案，并对囊胚进行PGS筛查，
从而减低梁太太再次胎停流产的风险，获得健康的孩子。
此外，医生建议梁先生夫妇进行生殖心理咨询，
以使他们有良好的心理建设面对医学方案。

Mr. And Mrs. Liang followed their doctor's advice and made an appointment for reproductive counseling.

The reproductive counselor told Mr. and Mrs. Liang, lots of infertile patients could benefit from IVF treatment but it involves complicated procedures. Good marriage relationship is the key issue to build up a positive attitude for all those treatments. Therefore, they should have same orientation for choosing this program, and build up a good understanding of individual differences in the effects of IVF treatment to establish an appropriate expectation on medical results. In most of the cases, all the medical procedures only proceed on female partner, so husband's care and support are the most positive strength to overcome medication discomfort and stress during the treatment.

梁先生、梁太太听从了医生的建议，在启动IVF方案前预约了生殖心理咨询。

生殖心理顾问告知梁先生、梁太太，IVF方案能造福众多不孕不育患者，
但治疗过程较为复杂，因此夫妻关系是建立良好就医心理的关键。
他们需在方案启动前具备一致的就医意愿，同时需理解IVF治疗方案存有个体差异，
对诊疗结果应建立恰当的心理预期。由于生殖医学方案仅实施在女性身上，
因此丈夫的陪伴和关爱，是克服用药不适和压力的最积极力量。

Mr. and Mrs. Liang decided to go through the IVF program together!
Mr. Liang took really good care of Mrs. Liang during the cycle and
accompanied her to visit the clinic every time.
Mr. Liang held Mrs. Liang's hand tightly until she woke up from the
surgery on the egg retrieval day.
The IVF doctor collected Mrs. Liang's eggs from her ovaries and
fertilized by Mr. Liang's sperm. After 5 days embryos development
and further testing, they finally had their healthy embryos and ready to transfer!

梁先生、梁太太共同决定选择IVF方案。
在IVF诊疗周期实施的过程中，梁先生无微不至的照顾和陪伴梁太太的每次就医。
取卵手术日，梁先生一直在病房紧握着梁太太的手等待她术后苏醒。
IVF医生将梁太太的卵子取出，和梁先生的精子结合形成受精卵，
随后培育成5天囊胚，最后经筛查他们终于拥有了属于自己的
健康胚胎并准备移植！

Embryo Transfer Day-Mr. Liang stayed with Mrs. Liang in the transfer room, they witnessed the IVF doctor implanted the new life 'seed' in Mrs. Liang's uterus.

胚胎移植日-梁先生一直陪同梁太太，

他们共同见证了IVF医生将新生命的"种子"植入梁太太的子宫中。

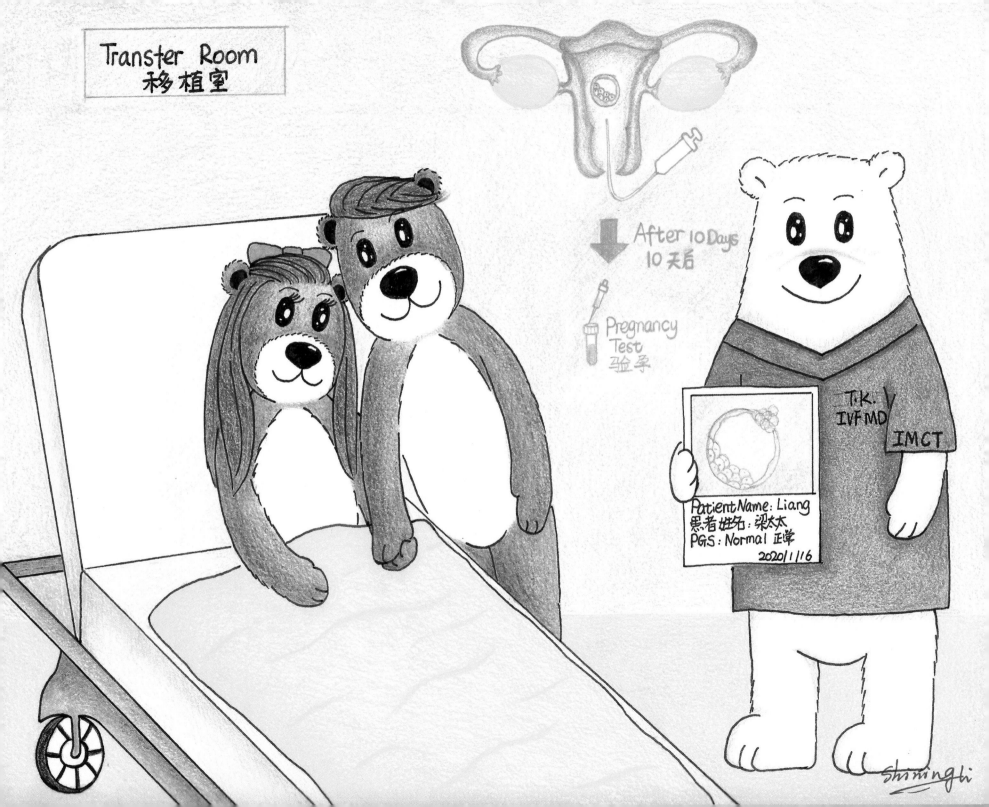

Pregnancy confirmed!

Healthy embryo, Happy pregnancy!

Under Mr. Liang's love and care, Mrs. Liang had a beautiful 10 months pregnancy journey.

梁太太成功受孕啦！

健康的胚胎，幸福的孕程。

在梁先生的关爱和照顾下，梁太太度过了10个月的美好孕期。

Mr. and Mrs. Liang's angel finally came to the world healthily!

Mrs. Liang appreciated Mr. Liang's all way support and care，

they accomplished an impressed IVF journey which sailed by love！

Mr. Liang, Mrs. Liang and their angle started a colorful new family life together!

梁先生和梁太太期盼已久的小天使终于健康诞生了！

梁太太感谢梁先生一路的相伴和支持，

他们共同历经了一段用爱承航的IVF之旅！

梁先生、梁太太和小天使一家三口共同开启了多姿多彩的家庭新生活！

Caring and Support

Thank you for reading this book.

If you are experiencing depression, feeling hopeless or lack of social and family support in infertility, you can seek support from us by contacting on support@imct-org.com. We are happy to listen your story and provide you with the solution to help you get through your difficulties together.

关爱与支持

感谢您阅读此绘本。

若您因不孕症而感到沮丧、绝望，或因缺乏社会和家庭支持而感到无助，您可通过support@imct-org.com与我们获得联系，我们乐意聆听您的故事，并为您提供帮助，与您共同面对和解决困难。

ISBN 978-0-578-76828-1

52169

9 780578 768281

CPSIA information can be obtained at www.ICGtesting.com
Printed in the USA
LVIW011821111120
671366LV00003B/51